RUSTY'S FOAL

RUSTY'S FOAL

by SUE GIBSON

PONY PRESS
ELLIS HORWOOD LIMITED
Publishers · Chichester

First published in 1981 by

ELLIS HORWOOD LIMITED

Market Cross House, Cooper Street, Chichester, West Sussex, PO19 1EB, England

Typeset in Baskerville by Ellis Horwood, Ltd., Chichester
Printed in Great Britain by R. J. Acford Ltd., Chichester

© 1981 S. Gibson

British Library Cataloguing in Publication Data

Gibson, Sue.
    Rusty's Foal.

    1. Thoroughbred horse.
    2. Horse breeding.
    I. Title.
636.1'32   SF293. T5
ISBN 0-85312-478-7

Rusty and her foal

Contents

Hurst Grange Nanette

Acknowledgements

My thanks to the Thoroughbred stallion, Nanette's sire, Music Major, and his owner Sue Harris; to Rusty, even more, for Nanette; to Nanette, for all the fun and everything she taught me; to my family, for publishing the book; to *Pony* magazine, for publishing the articles; to Bob, for typesetting; Don, for proofreading; to Rosanna, for her help; to Mr. Blake, for his thoughtfulness; to Lisa, for her care; to Jennie Loriston-Clarke, MBE, FBHS, for a happy ending and promising beginnings; to my husband's friends who sent cards, flowers and fruit and came a-visiting all summer; and to Brian, for his encouragement.

This book first appeared as a series of articles in *Pony* magazine, and the publishers are indebted to *Pony* magazine for their kind permission to reproduce the articles and photographs.

Some of the photographs in this book were taken by Rosanna Leon, and some by the author and her husband Brian Gibson.

Foreword

It was a lovely surprise to hear from Sue Gibson that Rusty's foal was for sale and that she was looking for a suitable home where the foal would have a chance to prove her potential.

The foal, Nanette, is a very well made filly with good limbs and bone and we hope she will be a useful member of our Stud. The Thoroughbred cross Welsh Cob is an ideal combination, with an excellent temperament, good active paces, and usually stands 15.1 hands high and over.

In her first winter with us, she will be companion to one of our home-bred fillies, and when she is three we hope to breed one foal from her before breaking her in. Eventually, we hope she will replace our dear Magic Lantern, who is now 19 years old, a wonderful eventer and advanced dressage horse who has been the main schoolmaster at Catherston Stud for many years.

We are all very much looking forward to Nanette's arrival this autumn and hope she will enjoy her life with us in the New Forest.

August 1981   Jennie Loriston-Clarke, MBE, FBHS

This book is dedicated to
Nan *1881–1981*

Author's Preface

When I had put Rusty in foal, I searched in vain for a little book that would tell me something of what to expect throughout the business of foaling, and rearing a foal. There were plenty of books on the subject, but none of them was simplistic enough to put my mind at rest about what was ahead; I decided then that I would put my experience down on paper in straightforward and, hopefully, enjoyable terms. This is not to say that foaling is a simple business, only relatively so, and not to be undertaken lightly. You are left, at the end of the day, with a living creature that needs to be fed, watered, trained, and all this costs money and needs a degree of knowledge. It is not profitable unless you are lucky enough to have plenty of spare fields and grow your own crops to feed your horses, because you have to pay rent for a foal, just the same as any other horse. But your pleasure is your profit, and if you are prepared to accept this, then you will gain a fortune in fun, watching a foal grow, and watching its mother's delight in her offspring.

So I have written this little book, firstly in the form of a series of articles for the top-selling equestrian monthly magazine *Pony*, and now in complete form, at a price which I hope horse lovers can afford. It gave me enormous pleasure to breed and rear my first foal, and almost as much to recount the experience in these pages.

Being lucky enough to find a home for my foal with a person of Jennie Loriston-Clarke's standing in the horse world means that, all things being fair and equal, my foal's future is in safe hands. It gives Nanette a chance of being a credit to the Catherston Stud; as well as to us, her breeders; and above all, her mother, Rusty.

Now let me take you back to the *real* beginnings of the story of Rusty's foal . . .

The author with Rusty and Nanette

1

What Have You Got There?

The Range Rover screeched loudly to a halt beside me and Farmer Harris poked his head out of the window, grinning from ear to ear in disbelief. "What have you got there?" he yelled, looking at the horse I was leading. "Looks like something from the gypsy's cart!"

He was quite right, as it happened, offended though I felt at the time to hear the fact voiced quite so abruptly. Farmer H. roared noisily off again, as he usually does; it's quite rare for him to drive anywhere *quietly*. I contemplated both his words and the object of his derision at the same time, and looked at my husband, who had witnessed the little cameo silently. It became an expression we were often to use in connection with Rusty, the bay Welsh Cob mare about whom Farmer Harris had just asked "What Have You Got There?" — sometimes, when Rusty was looking particularly sleek and well-groomed, as she did for her debut in showing, at Hickstead, all glossy and beautiful and well, Brian would smile quietly to me and say, "What Have You Got There?" I could smile, then, too, and feel a surge of love for this bay mare that has given us, during our years together, so much pleasure.

But the day Farmer Harris first said it, you would have agreed with him that I must have been out of my mind to buy her. She looked a proper starvation case, for a start, because she had been left out in a field without grass and without food for most of the winter. Added to this, her mane and tail were chopped almost out of existence, because when she had been rescued, they were too matted and thick with brambles to be dealt with in any other way. She had an acute case of dandruff, her coat stared without shine, and little sores bore evidence of rain spots. She was a hairy skeleton, to cut a long story short, and I had just spent £250 of my hard-earned income to buy her. It was because she was *quiet*.

My nerve had been well and truly shattered in recent months, breaking in and riding a grey mare which eventually was diagnosed to have a condition known as nymphomania, which makes a mare even more difficult to ride than a riggy gelding — nymphomania means the mare has cysts on her ovaries, and only a massive internal operation is the answer, a sort of equine hysterectomy, while a riggy gelding is one who has not been castrated properly and shows a lot of the traits of a stallion, without the nice bits. My experience with a nymphomaniac mare had driven me to the point where I would have bought a giraffe if I had been advised it would be a quiet ride, or a hippopotamus, come to that!

The same, placid,
sweet-natured mare throughout

So here I was with a hairy birdcage of a horse on four legs, and yet she stood beside me quietly throughout the hail of insults, and throughout the screeching of tyres and brakes as Mr. Harris arrived and departed. She just gave a big sigh as if to say "I'm Tired, Let's Go Back To The Stable." We had only walked a hundred yards or so, but it was obviously far enough for Bones, as someone unkindly nicknamed her.

Five months later, she was another matter. She stood a well-rounded, sturdy fourteen hands and two inches to the wither, sported a long thick mane and a long thick tail. She was a bouncing bag of health, and had given me back my riding confidence in a wonderful way — we rode together anywhere — all over the Sussex downs, flying things in our path like logs and small hedges, and the conviction I had had, deep down inside me, when I very first saw her, that she was just the horse for me, had been confirmed time and time again. She was even safe enough for my Jack Russell, Muppet, to ride!

September the same year almost brought tragedy, when the mare cracked her pelvic bone and had to spend four months in her stable (not even allowed out for mucking out), another month in a strawed-down cattle yard, and was finally turned out again in the following April. But the time served to draw me and the

Safe enough for Muppet to ride

Rusty

mare as close together as I will ever come to a horse, and the fact remains that, during all those long, lonely months of confinement, she never once developed a trace of a bad habit or a vice — she never bit, or kicked, or lost her temper, or began crib-biting and weaving. She remained the same placid, sweet-natured mare throughout.

The summer of 1978, therefore, saw us enjoying life together as usual, and the next couple of years went on without a hitch. But I felt there was one special thing that I wanted Rusty to do, before she was too old, and that was to have a foal.

I looked long and hard into the possibilities before making a final decision, and one of the original intentions was that I would bring the foal on myself until it was five or six, and then retire Rusty to stud, and use her offspring as my riding horse. This was not to be, as things turned out, and I was obliged in the end to sell the foal — and lucky enough to find the perfect home.

I didn't buy any foaling books *before* I made the decision. It was just as well, because when she was confirmed in foal, and I did go out and buy some books on foaling and the like, they terrified me. Not one of them really put my mind at rest, because they seemed to be talking about a category of horse that was not Rusty's type — she is a sturdy, broad-beamed family pony, and the mares in the books were beautiful slender thoroughbreds who needed nurturing from beginning to end.

The books seemed to give the impression that almost everything could go wrong, and showed dozens of photographs and drawings of incorrect presentations, and in the end only one book gave me any courage to go on. It was the book that eventually turned out to be correct about the foaling date, and in fact

Sturdy, broad-beamed family pony

wasn't a book devoted solely to the foaling business at all, but a general horse encyclopaedia with a small breeding section.

So my policy was, basically, leave her to it. Feed her the best grass, exercise her lightly, because it helps muscle; don't go thundering up hill and down dale (though people do, and their foals are still born well and strong); feed her with the best oats I could afford; make sure she always had clean bedding, top quality hay (musty hay, they said, makes a mare abhort!); that she didn't get kicked; that she was wormed regularly; and no fancy vitamin injections to boot. I adopted exactly the same policy, in fact, that I had for my Jack Russell bitch who produced seven fat healthy puppies at six weeks, instead of at seven — I had refused to stuff her with expensive vitamin pills, just fed her the best I could buy, and plenty of it, and it worked.

Another reason we decided to put our cherished family pony mare in foal, was because I thought: she's rising eight, and it's now or never. Another year could be too late; it was much better for her to have her first foal at nine than at ten.

The author's husband on Rusty

The author with Rusty

We flagged down Farmer Harris's pretty wife, Sue, one sunny April day as she drove (quietly) up the lane in her Land Rover, and booked Rusty's place in the field, where Sue's own brood mares run at grass all summer with her stallion. The stallion, Music Major, is a handsome 16.2 liver chestnut son of Queen's Hussar, who also sired Brigadier Gerard, and the Queen's Classic winner Highclere. Major's mother, Minstrel Queen, had died shortly after Major's birth — and she was a daughter of Tudor Minstrel, who was a son of Tudor Melody, and he was a son of Owen Tudor, and Owen Tudor won the Derby in 1941. Owen Tudor's father was one of the all-time great racehorses, and great racehorse sires, Hyperion, who won the Derby in 1933, as well as the Chester Vase, the Prince of Wales's Stakes, and the St. Leger Stakes. He was Champion Sire for six years and when he died in 1960, at the fine old age of 30, his offspring had won 752 races worth a total of precisely £633,520. 12s. 2d. That figure must have increased since 1960.

What was particularly endearing about Music Major's great, great, great grand-father was his physique. Hyperion wasn't a strapping great fellow, all muscle and grit, but a small horse, and as a foal there had even been talk of putting him down, he was such a poor little chappie. He was less than 15.2 hands high, and had only 7¾ inches of bone — and you know how the professionals like to talk about 9 inches of bone as though it were some kind of achievement for a horse to have big legs! In Hyperion's first race, at Doncaster, he was a 25–1 outsider and his trainer didn't bother to go all that way to see him run. He came fourth. Next time, he ran at Ascot and streaked home by three lengths from a field of 22. He went from strength to strength thereafter.

But all that is a long, long way off now. In 1980, 20 years after Hyperion disappeared to Trapalanda (the Heaven of the Horse), a Welsh Cob mare commonly known as Rusty, set off in a horsebox to marry one of Hyperion's innumerable offspring. Don't ask me now whether I would go through the business of foaling my mare again, because I just don't know. You would have to ask Rusty, I think, instead.

2

Wedding Bells

Music Major, as I have already said, runs with his mares at grass for the summer months, and so the often-clinical business of equine courting and mating could be carried out in the wide-open spaces below the Sussex Downs. The horses could please themselves how they went about it, which I felt was more natural than "in-hand" mating — I didn't want anyone forcing my Rusty into a cold-blooded marriage of convenience!

Major wouldn't match up, in terms of looks, to the type of Thoroughbred stallion you see all pouffed up and dancing elegantly around on a stallion bit at a Proper Stud Farm. He is an Outdoor Horse, a farmer's stallion, and he can quite often be seen half-asleep (presumably from his exertions) in a sunny corner of his field, all covered in Sussex mud where he's had a good roll on his back. But he is a *kind* type, a gentlemanly stallion on the whole, who is ridden during the winter months — and he throws some nice big foals. I had been well acquainted with his offspring, having bought one of his early foals and brought her on to a three-year-old in the past, and I knew the Major temperament was invariably passed on. Rusty's temperament is *faultless*, which is the main reason I bought her in the first place, and the two together ought, by the law of averages, to produce something that not only looked nice — Welsh cross Thoroughbred — but that would be, like its parents, kind. No-one wants a pig of a horse, even if it is still a foal.

The day arrived for the introduction of Rusty to her first, and I hope only, husband. I spent a nervous morning having my hair cut, because I didn't want Rusty to be ashamed of her scruffy owner, and recklessly told Lynn to take off as much as she liked. She did, and I sat, later, waiting for the horsebox to arrive, feeling sick on two accounts instead of just the one. Firstly, my hair seemed much too short and I was afraid my husband would moan, and secondly, what if this marriage *didn't* work? Suppose she didn't like Major; or he didn't like her; or she wouldn't come into season; or the other mares kicked her out of the field in a fit of jealous rage? I felt terrible, and probably looked it, because Sue Harris, the farmer's wife who owned Major, when she arrived with the horsebox to load us up, laughed at the sight of me. "You look worried," she said. "No make-up on yet," I told her.

Rusty loaded into the box like a dream, but then she is pretty good at most of the things you see mentioned in advertisements: 100% in traffic (mice frighten her more than juggernaut lorries); jumps; is good to box, shoe, catch (usually), bombproof, and so forth. The Land Rover and trailer lurched out of the farmyard

a farmer's stallion   Rusty

and headed south towards the Downs. Lit up by early spring sunshine and all breaking out with new green, the hills looked as stunning a picture as you would see if you went anywhere in the world. By the time I came to fetch Rusty home again, it would be summer.

We pulled into the field entrance, and within seconds the gate was surrounded by horses. A dozen or so nosey old broodmares fussed around each other. They were all about to foal, and their great bellies swung heavily as they milled around us — but their husband, obviously A Man of Authority where his mares were concerned, shooed them out of the way because he knew the routine of old; a horse box, any horse box, that pulled into that entrance way was, as far as he was concerned, loaded up with another mare for his harem.

He whinneyed impatiently, and said: "Come on, let me see what you've brought me this time". I got out of the Land Rover, pushed him gently back, and then gradually opened the gate for the trailer to slip quickly through into the field. But there was no danger of the horses running *out* of the gateway; they were far too interested in following the trailer into the field, to see what it contained. The little herd trotted alongsides, until Sue drew to a halt some hundred yards out into the field. I felt worse than ever, worse than I had felt for years. I felt as though I was selling Rusty down the river, though for what reason that emotion overcame me, I know not.

Sue unhooked the back of the trailer and let me go inside to Rusty, who had

The author with Music Major

travelled beautifully calmly, and stood waiting quietly. Sue instructed me not to clip the leadrope onto Rusty's headcollar, but to slip the rope through a ring, and hold one end of the rope in each hand. When I turned Rusty round and led her out of the trailer, and she veered excitedly away (she does get excited about certain things, like mice and stallions), I let one end of the rope go (the opposite end to the clip, of course); and it slid harmlessly through the ring until she was free. She was off!!

"Wow", I heard Rusty say as she took in the situation. Lush, lush grass, the richest pasture you could wish for — much too good for horses — and rolling hills where the fields swept away from the road, a little wood for shelter, and just take a look at the talent! She kicked up her heels and set off in a bouncy, beautifully arch-necked canter and the herd went with her.

Rusty fancied Major from the start but he, according to tradition, did not intend to be remotely interested in her at first. She was *not* in season, therefore she was of no use to him, and he wanted her *out*. He chased her off, rather viciously I thought, though Sue told me this is how all horses carry on in near-natural conditions, and he wouldn't hurt her really. I was not convinced, and worried all the way back in the Land Rover. Sue made me a nice cup of tea, and gave me a biscuit, and a cutting of her best purple lilac tree — it didn't help much at the time, though the cutting is doing splendidly, thank you.

"You ought to stay away for a week at least," Sue advised me, sagely as it turned out. Well, that's all very well when you have other horses to keep you occupied at home, but Rusty was my One-and-Only, and when I woke up next morning, my first instinct was to go and see how she was getting on. I was in for a shock and I wished that I had taken Sue's advice.

Rusty was grazing, half a mile from the herd. She looked up, slightly wild-eyed, when she heard my familiar car, as though she had been listening for nothing else all night long. It broke my heart the way she came tearing thankfully across the field to where I stood. I jumped into the field, heedless and ignorant of danger, and we rushed into each other's arms. She was trembling. "Please take me back," she said to me, "I've had enough of this! He's a beast, and I am not going to marry him, so we might as well get started for home straight away." I had brought her some bread, which she loves, and she ate it up and followed, clinging to me like a leech, as I walked back to the gate. I flung my arms once more round her neck and then dashed off, and as she watched my car disappear I wanted to burst into tears. Stupidly, without knowing it, I had got Rusty into trouble — because next morning, like a moth to a flame, when I went back to the gate, I saw what my attentions to her had meant. The stallion, very annoyed that she had been eating something or other that he had not, and that she had done something without his express permission, had bitten her quite hard on the neck. I shovelled some fly-repelling wound powder into the cuts, which looked nasty, and only just escaped from the field in time, because Major obviously thought Rusty was getting something else that he was not!

He came at her, teeth at the ready, but Rusty wasn't waiting around for another dose. She only has to be told something once! She galloped straight off up into the hills and stayed there. My heart bled for her, and I dashed off to see Sue. "I want to take Rusty back right away," I said.

Sue just laughed. "This is only part of the way that horses behave in the wild," she told me, not harshly. "Be patient. Once she is in season, she'll be OK." I could not argue with her superior knowledge, and went home feeling terribly depressed. I missed Rusty, dreadfully, and wished like mad that I'd never had the stupid idea of putting her in foal in the first place. It was almost the end of the first week before, miraculously, there was a change.

Rusty had been edging her way nearer and nearer to the herd and Major wasn't chasing her off quite so emphatically — just laying his ears back and poking his head at her threateningly. And then, one day, when I went up there, expecting a repeat of the first day, she *ignored* me. I felt like Mum at School Speech Day wearing a particularly dreadful hat, whose daughter is so ashamed that she pretends I'm not her Mum at all. How fickle these horses can be!

There was no mistaking the signals. Rusty was In Love, and she followed Major around like a lovesick schoolgirl, hanging on his every move and, every so often, giving him the old come-on. I felt mixed emotions — relief, because the mate I had chosen for her had finally accepted her and met with her approval; and pique, because she now had no further use for me. As I approached her tentatively, bread at the ready, she trotted determinedly off in the opposite direction. I called her a three-letter word and went back and sat in my car to watch.

I waited there for some time, and went back several times to watch, but nothing happened of any consequence on those occasions, and I never did witness

the actual mating of Major and Rusty. But for five solid days Rusty spent all her time idolising her husband, moving step-for-step with him like a shadow, and I'm quite sure it must have got on his nerves no end. Until, just as suddenly as she had fallen in love, she fell back out of it. She was In Foal.

Now, although Rusty had declared herself In Foal, and stopped taking any interest whatsoever in her husband, it did not mean she had started taking a re-newed interest in me. She was completely absorbed now in a mare called Emma (who belonged to my friend Sandy) and wherever Emma went, Rusty went too. They spent their days together in the sun, chatting about babies and natal care and I expect Emma told Rusty a thing or two about having foals — Emma had already had two, and she knew the ropes. I swear I saw them knitting booties and foalslips at one stage. But I still couldn't get anywhere near Rusty, though Emma remembered me and wanted my bread. Rusty stayed behind her, just out of reach, but at least I was able to check her for cuts and grazes, albeit from a distance. Rusty would go to Sue Harris without any trouble ("in fact, she's a flipping nuisance when I'm trying to feed Major!" Sue complained); but she ran a mile from me. Perhaps she associated me with getting into trouble from the stallion, or maybe she liked it here in the Maternity Ward so much that she didn't want me taking her back to her old field. I felt terribly hurt, whatever the reason for her rejection.

I left Rusty in the Maternity Ward for a further month after her week in season, to see if she came into season a second time — which would mean she had not "taken" the first time, and needed longer with the stallion. The month came and went, and Rusty showed no further interest in Major whatsoever, and so we assumed all was well; how I hated that month, with no Rusty to get up and see to each morning, or put to bed at night. Her stable was a hollow, empty place and I hardly went near it until the day before she came back, when I laid a soft new straw bed, filled a big haynet, water bucket and feed bucket; and went off with Sue to fetch her home.

When we pulled into the field, I kept out of sight in the cab until Sue had caught Rusty. Then I grabbed Rusty — who looked shocked at my trickery — and while Sue fed Major, I popped Rusty into the trailer and off we went.

The months of waiting began, and with it, several variations in Rusty's temperament. She was tested in foal twice, once in September, and again in January. She behaved like a silly brood mare sometimes, instead of being a placid quiet old duck, and she could be flighty, thoroughly silly and very irritating. My friend Erica just laughed: "You wouldn't be laughing if your horse ran away from you," I said unpleasantly. But Erica kept on laughing and despatched her daughter Sharon to be the Rusty-Catcher-in-Chief.

It is *frightfully* humiliating when your friend's small daughter can walk up and catch your pony, when that same pony only has to catch sight of you in the distance with a leadrope in your hand, to run off, wagging her head naughtily, to the furthest corner of the field. It made me see red, I can tell you.

So I resorted to my old plastic bread bag trick, which I rustle to attract Rusty's attention. Having heard the rustle, she stops and looks at the bag. I walk away with it, stomach triumphs over mind (she *adores* bread), she trots after me, and I catch her.

I fed her all the goodies, like best oats, Equivite, milk pellets, best hay, reading that this, or that, would help her build up a nice foal and help her not to lose condition. Don't let her get too fat, said one friend. Don't let her lose weight, said another.

"Why on earth," I asked myself, severely, "does anyone ever bother to try to have a foal?"

The answer was not far off.

3

Now You Have Got Two Horses!

Rusty kept us guessing about her delivery date, as her time grew near. She had a special, secretive look about her, as though she knew everything, but was going to keep us guessing. You can wait until I am ready, she seemed to say, I'll choose my own moment for this. Be patient.

We were patient, although I do confess in odd moments, I found myself wondering if there really was a foal there at all! Two vets had confirmed it, and after her early scatty phase, she had settled down again and was even more tractable and loving than before. She did show the odd sign of irritation when I fussed her, on days when she felt Too Pregnant For That Sort of Thing; and, like Topsy, she grew and grew and grew. She would waddle off into her field in the mornings like a squat, swaying walking mushroom; and then march stroppily up and down past the gate, looking at her watch, irritated, if I was much later than 4 p.m. in the evenings to bring her back indoors for the night! She loved her bed, and lay down a lot more as time went on — until, with about two months to go, she was simply too fat, and had to sleep standing up! Horses do, you know — they kind of lock their legs into a comfy position, set their neck muscles and close their eyes and go to sleep, like hens do on a perch.

I rode her a little because my vet advised it. We had some very pleasurable pregnant plods round the lanes, watching early lambs bouncing about and generally almost falling asleep together as we went on our leisurely way. We never went far, particularly after the ride when my friend Rosanna reminded me that I was astride two horses, not one!

In the local village pub, Rusty's Foal became quite a talking point, and a sweepstake was organised by Ron, the Landlord, as to the exact colour of the foal at birth. I gave him a list of the real possibilities, and our friends chose a colour and put £1 in the kitty, winner takes all — the colours varied from liver chestnut to light bay. I didn't put in any silly colours, like piebald or skewbald. I should have had a fit if Rusty's Foal were a painted pony! Not that I don't like painted ponies — I'd have just got into awful hot water in the pub! Boiled in cider, they all said.

I also had a long list of friends and relations who wanted to be telephoned *the very minute* the foal arrived, and it got quite exciting — mind you, private worries stalked my sleep, like foals with two heads, five legs, and a lot of very silly notions constantly flitted through my head like buzzing gnats. We also, at this time, moved Rusty to a farm nearer our home — we could walk to see her now, in 15 minutes, which was something I had always yearned — you never can tell, when you have to rely on a car, if you'll always be able to get to your horse!

The foaling books did not agree about a date. The first one had a useful-looking dial on the back. When you pointed a black arrow to the last possible service date, a red arrow simultaneously pointed to the Big Day. "Probable foaling date" it said. Probable was the right word — it allowed 11 months *minus* four days. The encyclopaedia with the breeding section allowed 11 months *plus* four days, and the difference between the two amounted to over a week! To be safe, of course, we presumed it to be the first of the two dates, and kept an anxious watch as the moment grew near.

Rusty's chest deepened and her muscle slackened off to the point of being positively floppy. Her udder filled like a balloon with milk, but there was no sign of the "waxing-up" — the name given to the stage at which milk begins to slowly secrete from the udder, to form "waxy" blobs on the teat. It usually means that birth is imminent within 36/48 hours, although someone cheerily said her mare waxed up at 6 p.m. and foaled at 8.30 the same night! As it happened, 11 months minus four days came and went without event.

The farmer, Mr. Blake, whose grazing and stable we now rented, took a late, late look at Rusty for us each evening, checking his sheep as he went. He said he'd brought pretty well every species of living creature into the world and ought to recognise the signs of restlessness. He even ran out to Rusty in the middle of a thunderstorm at five one morning, because thunderstorms occasionally bring cows into calf — but Rusty never worries about thunder, only mice, and he found her munching hay, docile as ever. He had got wet for nothing and next morning he asked me, politely, was I *really* sure she was in foal? Cows can have phantom pregnancies, he told me. That worried me, and if I had not been able to see a small being kicking vigorously away at its mother's womb when its mother drank, I would have agreed with him and begun to assume that the whole pregnancy was just a phantom, an excuse Rusty had invented to avoid being ridden too often!

The first book proved, in Rusty's case, quite wrong, and the second book proved almost exactly right. Eleven months plus six days after her last known service date, Rusty produced a nine hands high, 175 pound filly foal, the colour of soft fudge, with the texture of a kitten. Actually, in waiting the extra two days, Rusty had unknowingly done me an enormous good turn. On the right date, which was Easter Sunday, my much-loved grandmother died at the age of 99, only one month from her hundredth birthday, and Rusty held on to that foal an extra two days. For the foal to have arrived in the middle of my first moments of grief would not have been appropriate, and it was as if Rusty *knew*. My grandmother's name was Emma, but I had never known her as Emma — and so we decided to call the foal Nan, or Nanette (Hurst Grange Nanette, as she officially became upon registration as a Welsh cross Thoroughbred) after Nanny.

We had done quite a bit of staying up late, and late night visiting, and telephoning our farmer, Mr. B. in the middle of the night, and I was pretty exhausted. There *were* spots of wax on her teats, but when Mr. B. advised me on Easter Monday night that Rusty was not at all restless and munching hay as usual, I went to bed and slept like a baby — mainly upon the advice of my vet, Sue, who had said right from the start that the best owners are those who leave their

a filly foal the colour of soft fudge, texture of a kitten

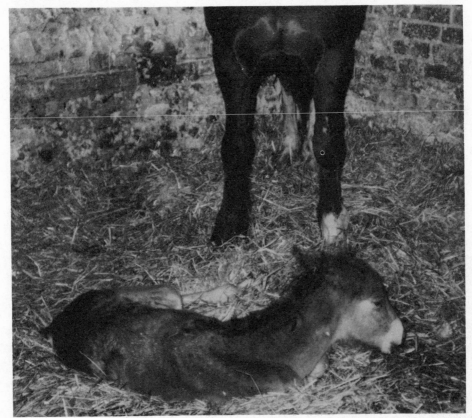

mares to produce their offspring in peace and quiet. I awoke early on Tuesday morning, thought of the Nan who had just gone, jumped up and rushed down to the stables and there, fresh, wobbly, soft, sleepy and wonderful, was the Nan who had just arrived.

Mind you, as I came into the yard, Mr. B. gave me an awful turn. He raised two fingers in Churchillian style, and grinned hugely. "What, twins?" I squawked in a panic!

"No, you have got two horses in your stable this morning!" he said. If you know anything about twin foals, you will understand my fears. One foal is quite enough of a handful, both for the mare and the human who have to raise it, and one foal was quite enough as far as I was concerned — and Rusty too, for that matter.

I had never bred a foal before, and neither had my mare, but she had coped quite beautifully, as Sue the vet predicted, with the arrival of Nan. She had stripped the caul, a fine membrane rather like a nylon stocking, which completely encases the foal at birth: if the caul is not stripped immediately the umbilical cord snaps, the foal will suffocate, because once the cord goes, the foal has lost

26

its lifeline to its mother, and must start breathing independently. Usually only very weak mares do not strip the caul, and it very often splits itself as the foal lands on the ground, anyway. Not all mares lie down to foal. Rusty had also expelled the afterbirth, as it turned out, although I was worried about this at first, not being able to find it in the straw. But my immediate concern was getting the foal to suckle.

Having come through the birth with flying colours, Rusty was now looking at this creature before her in the straw with some astonishment. I wasn't quite sure what to do next, except that, whatever it was, *not* to interfere too much. Nature takes its own course, Sue had said the night before.

So in this moment, that I had waited for for so long, I didn't quite know which course of action to take. The foal struggled to her feet and tottered, as though without sight, in the general direction of her mother's flanks. Rusty squealed in amazement as though it were a Real Live Spook, and jumped away, staring in amazement that the thing should have legs. The foal immediately fell

struggled to her feet and tottered as though without sight

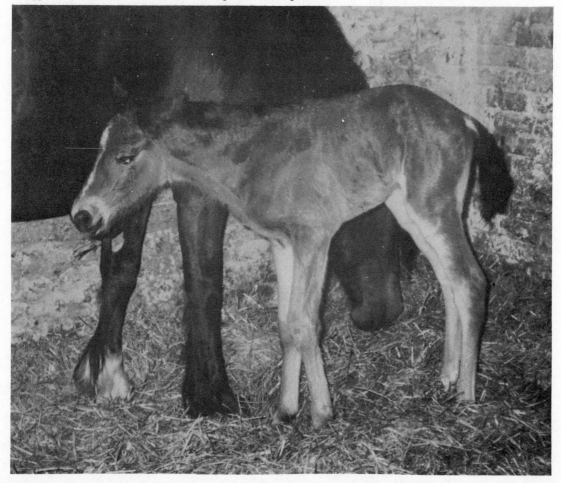

over, and lay there. I decided I ought to do *something*, so I put a headcollar on Rusty and, with Mr. B. at Rusty's head, I pushed the foal gently in the general direction of the milk supply. Rusty, pinned up against the wall, held firmly at the front end by Mr. B., and soothed by my voice, trembled. She unwillingly allowed her foal to nuzzle her teats, and we decided that that was enough human involvement, and I went home to fetch my husband to see the new arrival.

"She's done it," I yelled happily up the stairs to where he lay having a peaceful morning bath. Within seconds he was out, dried and dressed, and together we crept back to the stable. There was Rusty, eyes calm, ears pricked, gently licking her little girl's bottom as the foal suckled, noisily and hungrily.

"That first feed is important," I told Brian, knowingly. "That's the feed that contains colostrum, and it gives Nan the immunity she needs against the germs and viruses that she is exposed to now she is out in the world." It is *amazing* how sage you feel when you are talking to someone who knows almost nothing about horses, isn't it?

That first feed is important — Nanette at 2/3 hours

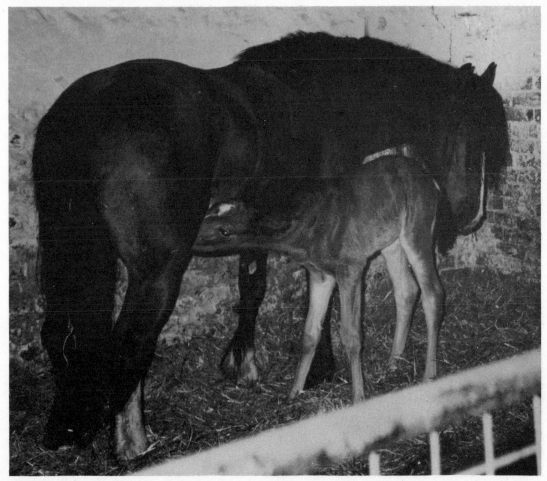

I gave Rusty a soft bran mash for a laxative, and we went home to breakfast. Rusty looked well, and I was sure the afterbirth was somewhere — but I would ask my vet to come down later in the morning, just in case. Besides, she wanted to see Rusty's Foal.

Wishing silently that one Nan had lived for long enough to know that now I had another Nan, I rang the vet. She giggled, pleased as I was that Rusty had pulled it off, and reminded me of her days at the Royal Veterinary College in London. The College had brought in ten Highland mares, all due to foal, and put them in special foaling boxes with one-way windows so that the students could observe a natural foaling. The horses had other ideas, however, and one-way mirrors don't hide veterinary students from foaling mares, because foaling mares have a sixth sense about the presence of human beings. The students kept a vigil by rota for *sixty days* over those ten mares and no-one, but no-one, saw a birth. Every time a student popped out to the loo, or staggered gasping to the coffee machine for a drink, a mare would pop out her foal. The mares just *knew*.

I went back to the stables and began to muck out around Rusty and Nan, because I really wanted to find that afterbirth. It is very important for a mare to expel the afterbirth within two hours of the arrival of her foal, because if not, a feverish condition sets in and your mare can be dead within a few hours if professional help is not sought — I don't wish to put the frighteners on readers, but ignorance of this kind could be fatal. As could ignorance about the presentation

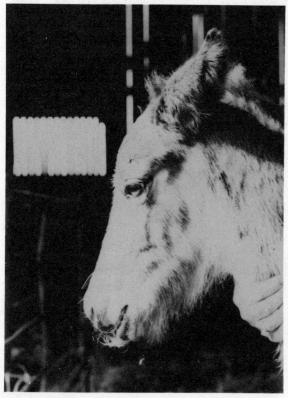

What a Treasure!

at birth — a foal's feet should come out first, together, with the nose following lying flat on the legs (if you are lucky enough to witness it, which few are) — any other way, just call the vet, because if you tug those feet, and the foal slips back inside, and you have broken the caul, the foal will drown — so the rule of thumb is, leave well alone. You wouldn't expect a vet to do your job if you were a car mechanic, or a hairdresser, and you should not expect to play at vets during foaling.

Then I found the afterbirth. Oh what a clever, clever mare! She had buried it most carefully in deep straw, just as a mare in the wild would attempt to do, to cover the traces of the birth from preying creatures. I donned rubber gloves, and put it carefully into a container for my vet to check. This afterbirth must be in one piece — even if only a small part of it is not expelled, the fever sets in.

I had read somewhere that if you find the milt from a foal's mouth, and keep it to dry out, it will always bring you luck. I looked eagerly as I mucked out for this small round substance, like a pebble, which stops the foal from sucking fluid down into its lungs when it is in the womb. It is rarely found, and I searched in vain.

Sue, the vet, arrived a few minutes later, and said "What a treasure!" of the newly-born foal. She was as delighted as me, almost; she weighed her, measured her; and took the mare's and the foal's temperature. She also checked that the foal had passed a small dropping — here again, they must pass that first dropping within hours of birth. Then she checked the afterbirth, grateful for my rubber gloves — you don't want to be squeamish to look at afterbirth, but when it has protected and held your foal safe for 11 months and six days, it's different, and I didn't feel at all sick. It was fascinating in fact, and there are yards of the stuff — foal-shaped, of course. Sue checked that it was all there and we were just about to return it to the container for disposal, when we spotted something round and brown. Yes, it was the milt.

4

First Steps

"It's your baby," I told Rusty firmly when she asked me what to do next. "You must get on with the business of bringing it up!" She looked a bit puzzled about the creature that she now shared her stable and her life with; she knew she ought to feed it, and did; she knew she ought to keep her eye on it, and did. But disciplining it was another matter, and she was immune to her foal's naughtiness, and was an over-doting mother in the early days.

Mr. B. kindly offered us a strawed-down cattle yard for the first two weeks of Nanette's life, which suited us admirably. I wanted to wait until Rusty had been through the "foaling heat," which is the week when a mare is in season following the birth of her foal. It often sours her milk, which makes the foal scour badly, and scouring, quite literally, burns the hair off a foal's backside! It is smelly, uncomfortable and can be avoided with certain care — and I was in a position, thanks to Mr. B.'s generosity, to take that care.

The next problem I encountered was getting Rusty and Nanette, without assistance, from their stable to the cattle yard. I thought that Nan would automatically follow her Mum out into the yard, but she did not. She just stood in the stable and yelled for help. So it was Nanette that I would have to lead, and let Rusty follow.

I put a little foalslip over Nan's head, overwhelming her indignant resistance. Luckily she was still small enough to be overcome in these early battles for supremacy! Then, with my left hand guiding her head, I pushed her firmly along with my right hand, muttering "walk on, walk on" encouragingly until she began to get the message. We also did "woah, woah" as well, because I felt it was just as important to learn to use the brakes as readily as the accelerator! Rusty followed anxiously, whickering "Please Be Careful, That's My Baby" and "Oh Do Watch Out", generally worrying herself silly. But we made it. Nanette had made her First Steps.

Nanette was remarkably quick to pick things up, and soon we could go for little walks across the yard in a threesome, me leading and pushing Nan, Rusty following, worried. Nan also learned it was fun to pick things up other than lessons — like the bucket, which she would pick up between her gums (no signs of teeth until she was a week old) and cart round the yard until something else caught her eye, like the string tying up the gate, or the haynet which she already tried sharing with Mum. She copied Mum a lot, and this helped us with teaching her to be caught. I was determined not to let her free in a field until I could catch her!

fun to pick things up between her gums

At first she fled from human beings, racing round behind her mother and then peering saucily out through mother's legs! I soon learned to corner her, get my arm firmly round her neck, and take hold of the foalslip. She struggled for the first few occasions, but soon realised it was easier to accept capture!

She learned to eat oats practically at once, playing with them in her mouth before swallowing them. She watched her mother plunge her head into the bucket, thought to herself This Is Worth A Try, and followed suit. I decided that, while she was still playing with hard feed, she could do best pinching what she could from her mother — and gave mother more, of course, to allow for the foal's theft. Nan was a disgustingly noisy eater, and put my Jack Russells in the shade for table manners — and I thought they were bad enough!

Our first walk outside the yard was twenty yards up the lane — we are lucky, there is only the occasional farm traffic, and dog walkers entranced by the dancing filly foal. Nan walked quite nicely, actually, considering her age, but then inexplicably decided she wanted to stay *here*. I pushed, I pulled, I cajoled, I got strict, but Nanette was glued to the ground, bonded like cement. Eventually I

pinching what she could from her Mother

pushed so hard that her back legs slipped from under her, and she sat down hard on her bottom in the lane. It seemed unkind to laugh, although my Jack Russells ran round in a circle laughing hysterically like hyenas — that did the trick, and surprised her into carrying on back to the stable with an element of decorum.

She soon got used to being groomed, because I ran a soft brush over her on the first day of her life. I also kindly thought I would save the blacksmith a job, by teaching her to stand with one foot held up, as soon as I felt she was safe on three legs. She showed some minor wrath, and backed up to her mother when we had finished, and kicked her in the shins. "Do something," we said to Rusty, "Bite her bottom, make her behave!" Rusty just munched on at her beautiful fresh-smelling haynet (I had to give her top quality hay, just as before, to keep the milk supply up to scratch), and said: "You do something. You wanted a foal, it was your idea, not mine!"

The little lane near the stables is gated both ends and I would walk mother and daughter down it so that Rusty could pick at grass. I usually held Nanette, teaching her that it is just as important to Stand Still and Be Patient While Your Mother Eats, as it is to walk on and whoa. She showed remarkable tolerance, and I thought that deserved some freedom. I let her off the leadrope and, after a few seconds, she looked carefully at me, then at her mother, then back at me, then performed a minor Irish jig, and took off down the lane after Mum. She suddenly realised she had reached Mum, and was fast overtaking Mum, and she slammed on all the anchors at once. Four feet splayed helplessly into four corners of the lane, Nanette lurched wildly for a few seconds, amazed at what was happening and then tottered there, obviously wondering how on earth to get out of

carried on back to the stable

Nanette

I ran a soft brush over her

It was a better try

such a funny position. Carefully, one by one, she brought each far-flung leg back into its correct place underneath her body! "What fun! Let's try it again!"

This time as she galloped up towards me, she planned ahead and got her brakes working as she reached me. All four feet splayed and her head rocked forwards, but it was a better try. Back to mother she went, getting just a little over-confident, and forgetting that this was downhill and adjustments needed to be made. They weren't quite, and she almost fell flat on her nose. Now a mother of a full week's standing and becoming rather blasé, Rusty carried on grazing.

After her initial shock, she never displayed any real surprise at the things her half-Thoroughbred daughter decided to do, and as long as Nanette was within sight Rusty was placid and trusting. I think she felt that as long as I was around, it was OK. She didn't object at all to the Jack Russells cavorting with her foal:

We went for walks round the stable yard

and I remembered the first time I had brought Rusty back to my stable, when she was only four years old herself. My dog, a tiny mischievous puppy, had hurtled round and round in the fresh, crackling straw and Rusty had never batted an eyelid. In that moment she had endeared herself to me for life and her tolerance of small yappy dogs had obviously been inherited by her daughter.

Rosanna helped me a lot during these early days, and it was also Rosanna who urged relentlessly that Rusty was a good enough Welsh Cob to show. I laughed outright the first time, thinking it was one of her jokes. But it wasn't. So we decided that if you are going to take a mare and foal to a show, what better introduction could there be for a foal, than Hickstead. Rosanna could throw stones right into the International Ring from her livery yard (though she doesn't), and we decided that, as part of Nanette's general education, we would enter them in a combined class.

Before I knew it, the entry form was completed, the entry fee paid, and I was, for the first time, an Exhibitor/Groom, instead of Press. Instead of scuttling round trying to winkle out subjects to interview I would be at the nerve-wracking end of the stick — the judged, rather than the onlooker.

In the meantime Nanette's education continued. We went for walks round the stable yard, inspecting the wheelbarrow and the dungheap, looked at the lambs who were growing faster by the minute; and peered curiously into other peoples' stables, at other peoples' horses. Nanette shared her mother's ridiculous fear of small white stones on the ground, and daintily side-stepped anything remotely pale in her path.

She was, as my farmer, Mr. B., put it, the Star Attraction. His farm is very close to the village and a stream of small girls and boys, Brownie packs and Cub packs, visit the farm each spring To See The Lambs. But the poor lambs were now overshadowed and for weeks previously every single child I met on the footpath had told me seriously and quietly, that they just couldn't wait for the foal to be born. Morning after morning they would go off in a devoted procession to see Rusty in her small, pre-foaling paddock. One child tried to give Rusty a potato to eat, which she didn't want, so I had to paint an unsightly notice saying Do Not Feed The Horses Because Foals Can Choke On Things. A small piece of apple or carrot could quite easily choke a foal to death, and Mr. B.

Rusty and Nanette, sharing a feed

delivered Rusty's Fan Club with a severe lecture. Next day, as though by way of an apology, I found Rusty in her field adorned with a beautifully and carefully-made daisy chain. I have kept it, of course.

When Nanette finally arrived, she kept the children entranced as she pranced and frisked her way round the covered yard. She bucked, cavorted and tossed her head and they laughed and clapped with glee. She was in imminent danger of becoming a frightful show-off.

But she came back to hand when she knew I meant business; I could not afford her to become a complete scatterbrain. After all, the day might come when she would have to be weaned from her mother, and found a new home — and if the time came for her to go, Rusty and I both felt Nanette should be a credit to her upbringing. She, of course, was blissfully unaware of plans for her future, and danced on to the applause — it seemed there was no end to her energy, and no end to the stream of admirers. "I just hope," I told Nan severely, "that you find as many admirers when you are older as you do now! The farm is one thing: Hickstead is another."

danced on to the applause

5

Nanette Goes to Hickstead

Nanette was growing fast. She was now 11 hands high, five weeks old, and came up to my waist. She was getting daily more strong and I was thankful that we had taught her the basics of good behaviour in her real infancy. She led, for the most part, easily; we could pick her feet up and clean them out without any fuss, and she stood quietly to be groomed and combed — the early hard work was paying off handsomely, and was to pay off more handsomely still, as things turned out.

Preparations for her Big Day at Hickstead began a week before the day of the show and we asked Mr. B. for the small paddock on the bank for Rusty and Nan, because the ground there drained quickly and there was little, if any mud — their usual field was still very boggy round the gateway, and their fetlocks became muddy when we took them in or out of this field. We did want white clean fetlocks for Hickstead, and the paddock on the bank solved the problem. It still rained a lot, even though it was almost June.

Rosanna had promised me her undivided attention for the day before the show, and the day of the show itself, and she was as good as her word. I had not done a drop of showing in my life, and she carried me through in full sail. If anything, I made her terribly nervous with my constant worrying and chattering and asking silly questions beginning with the very irritating words, "what if" — rather as I had driven Sue Harris, Music Major's owner, equally potty before I had taken Rusty to Major to be married. But Rosanna was as patient and firm as Sue had been over a year earlier — how that year had flown! — and I could not, or would not, have attempted it without Rosanna.

Derek the blacksmith arrived the morning before the show to put a pair of shoes on Rusty's front feet and shape her back ones. The stony track to the paddock was making her slightly sore on her fronts, where tiny flints and pebbles dug into the frog — the back feet, which do not carry as much weight as her front feet, did not seem to be affected, and only needed a manicure.

Nanette thought Derek was quite fascinating. She bit him quite hard to see how his green jacket tasted. I smacked her sharply and so she bit me as well. This trick had developed since she had learned to eat grass, and even though she thought nipping peoples' coats and gloves made for jolly entertainment, I had to teach her that it was not, so I smacked her again *on the side of her neck* — it is very bad to hit horses of any age around the face, as it makes them "head shy" and nervous of hands approaching their heads. You will sometimes see horses in sale rings move their head nervously away from the approaching hand of a pros-

Nanette was growing fast

pective buyer, and this is probably because at some time in their life, someone has hit them in the face. A slap on the neck was closer to the sort of punishment that another horse might mete out if she had bit it, instead; she looked a bit surprised, and went for another nip, but I was ready this time and hit her again down the neck with the strong admonishment "No!" The message went home, for the time being at least, and she lost interest and went off for a walk by herself round the paddock. That upset Rusty who started hopping about a bit, wondering where her daughter was going.

It was boiling hot; I should think it was the first hot day of 1981, summer though it was supposed to be. Rusty and Nanette both still lived indoors at night, because thunder storms kept brewing up and I was fed up with rushing down at 9.30 in the evenings to get them out of the storms. It was easier in the long run to get them in at about 7 p.m., and turn them out for the day at around 8.30 in the morning. Rusty is always spotlessly clean about her stable — she does all her droppings in the same place, and I swear she has a tidy-up in the mornings before I get down, so that the place is all spic and span for me to muck out! We call her Mrs. Tiggywinkle sometimes, she is so fanatically clean in her habits. She could almost live in our kitchen, she's so nearly house-trained! And the foal's minute contribution made little difference at that time to the amount of work involved — although this was to change dramatically.

After Derek went, because they needed the sun on their backs (which provides essential Vitamin D to horses) so badly, I left them in the paddock. Rosanna was coming after lunch to bath them, to make them look like show ponies instead of a slightly hairy Welsh Cob mare and foal — it would be fun, and cool us all down to play with water and shampoo on such a glorious day!

The moment we prepared the water buckets it began to rain

On the dot of two o'clock, as we prepared the water buckets and opened the Head 'n' Shoulders bottle, the sun disappeared dramatically behind a cloud and it began to rain. Luckily, we still had the occasional use of the covered yard where Rusty and Nan had spent their first two weeks together, but it was miles from the tap and hose! So Rosanna shampoo'ed and brushed and combed and scrubbed her heart out for three solid hours, and all I did was play bucket patrol: running to and from the water tap keeping Rosanna supplied with as much water as she needed. I was exhausted, and goodness knows how she must have felt, but by 5 p.m. that evening we were both glad to sit down for five minutes and polish off half a bottle of cider because we were too tired to make a cup of tea. I didn't know you had to be so *fit* to go showing, I said to Rosanna, not for the only time in the next 24 hours!

But things were getting done: Rusty's feet had been blacked, and shone; her mane and tail and coat shampoo'ed and beautifully combed through — and the mane all tied up in elastic bands until the morning, because we wanted to keep it lying to one side overnight. Like all Welsh Cobs, Rusty has a thick mane with a mind of its own, which prefers to part in the middle and fall both sides of her neck. This just would not do, said Rosanna, and Rusty spent the night looking as though she was wearing a string of carrots down her neck. Rosanna also bandaged her tail, but I bet Rusty had that off the minute we drove out of the yard, because it was well trampled into her bedding and buried deeply in the straw!

In common with probably everyone who shows horses, I had obtained some "bottled shine" and when I had put Rosanna's jodphurs and her white shirt into my washing machine — she'd been to busy to do them herself — and left them sluishing around in solitary grandeur, I went back down to the stables to give the dogs a walk and put on a first coat of this spray-on magic, instant shine. Rusty was quite silly about it, snorting like a daft old goat, and dancing left and right as I sprayed the stuff on and stroked it in with my hand. I recalled something I had read in a horsy book which said that giving oats to horses is like giving too much alcohol to people — it can make them go silly. Rusty was obviously drunk, I decided.

Like many good brood mares, Rusty had put her *all* into this foal. Every brood mare feeds her baby, but some do so more than others, and Rusty came into this latter category. The result was a slight tucking-up round her flanks, and a miniscule loss of condition; so I had been pumping oats and complete nuts (for fibre) into her as fast as I could. Constant rain had made the grass more water than protein and until the sun came out properly, and dried the ground up, when the quality of the grass would naturally improve, I had to continue pushing feed into the mare at a faster rate than the foal was taking it out via the milk supply . . . so Rusty was drunk with good food!

Nanette, however, was not drunk. An early lesson on being tied up and left within sight of her mother, but several yards away, paid off now. She had stood quite quietly, nibbling her rope, while we bathed Rusty and now, while her mother did an Irish jig to evade That Awful Spray Shine, Nanette didn't bat an eyelid. She still didn't move when her turn came for spraying, and in fact she put one of her back legs into the rest position and started to fall asleep. She enjoyed the sensation.

A final polish before Hickstead

We were all awake very early on the morning of the show. I went down and mucked out the worst of the stable, leaving the major job until later. I began brushing and adding more Instant Shine; Rusty seemed to have sobered up and accepted it more calmly. I was just wondering how to use up the rest of the morning — we weren't leaving for Hickstead until lunchtime — when a saddler rang to say the foal headcollars were in stock. I had been waiting *weeks* for this call and a diversionary drive to pick up a smart new brown headcollar helped use up nervous energy. I bought Rosanna a showing cane as a thank you present for her help, and then decided that as this was probably the only time I should appear in the show ring at Hickstead, it would be as well to look smart. My old hacking jacket, of which I was at least the fourth owner, kept popping open if I lifted my arms in the air for any reason, because I was so fat. So I purchased, at considerably idiotic expense, a brand new, properly-fitted hacking jacket. It didn't make me appear any slimmer, I noticed, but I was glad later on in the day that I wasn't wearing my old button-popper!

Rosanna arrived. We had two glasses of Dutch Courage (all the law allows drivers!) and went to the stables. We loaded up and drove the whole two miles to Hickstead — an important factor in the choice of a first show — and parked in the stable field and unloaded. Even so, it took about half an hour! We twittered nervously to each other about Comb That Mane Down Again and My White Gloves Are Missing and Where's The Chalk She's Got Another Green Stain and Let's Put More Blacking on That Hoof!

We walked down to the ring where Nanette spooked at *everything* — she had never been anywhere in the five short weeks of her life and her eyes popped out on organ-stops at the big show jumpers.

The showing part itself didn't take very long, as there was only a small turn-out. But Rosanna and I both learned a tip about showing a mare with a foal at foot! Rosanna had done a lot of showing and knew the ropes, but on the first occasion that the Judge asked us for a small show of our own, we thought it best for Rosanna to take Rusty first, and for me to follow with Nanette. It was *not* a good idea. The moment that her mother broke into a spanking show trot, Nanette broke into a spanking flat out unshowmanlike gallop, taking me completely by surprise. Luckily, at the last minute before entering the ring, I had tied a knot in the end of the white leadrope and this prevented Nanette from escaping me completely! My hat began to come loose. Nanette overtook Rosanna and Rusty like a highspeed motorboat, towing me in her wake like a drunken water skier, with one hand on the last inch of the leadrope, the other trying to keep my hat from falling off completely. A titter of laughter rippled round the ringside, and Rosanna's face, as I turned round to tell her, rather unnecessarily, that I couldn't stop, was a study.

In the ring at Hickstead, before Nanette took off with me

When Nan realised her mother was no longer trotting busily away from her, thankfully, she stopped. It was a near thing. We almost went out of the ring!

The two stallions, needless to say, took the first two places, and the Judge called for a re-run between Rustina and her remaining rival, a Section D palomino mare carrying rather more condition than looked good for her; so was I, and rather still gasping for breath after my unscheduled flight, I didn't trot the foal up the second time.

Instead, I walked the foal *away* from her mother, towards the corner of the ring where Rusty would finish her second run. Rusty, naturally anxious to get back to her precious (should we say precocious!) baby, trotted out quite beautifully, extending and arching her neck. I was so proud of What Have You Got There that I could have burst!

But the Judge preferred the other mare, and pinned the orange-and-yellow fourth place rosette on Rusty's bridle. I had never won a rosette before in my life. What better place to start, said Rosanna, than Hickstead? Then the judge pinned a blue winner's rosette on Nanette, for being the best foal in the Mountain and Moorland section. It was all amazing and a moment I could not have dreamed up — Nanette, unconcerned, first tried to eat her mother's rosette and then her own.

We let Nanette have a feed from her Mum, and Rusty had a good munch on the long grass at the edge of the collecting ring, while people took pictures of the foal looking adorable, in her winning rosette.

But it was with an enormous sense of relief that we loaded up for home. Feeling I owed it to them to travel back in their company, I climbed into the horsebox to share the homeward journey with the horses.

Rusty chomped on some hay, and stood quietly as the trailer turned for home. Nanette gave a deep, dreamy sigh, tucked her head lovingly under my arm, and I think, for a few moments at least, the Best Foal went to sleep.

When I got them home, Brian said to me: "What *Have* You Got There?"

Best Foal went to sleep

6

A Summer at Grass

Nanette during her
first summer at grass
— slow to lose her foal coat

We were not lucky with our summer weather and Nanette was slow to lose her "foal coat". It was wet and cool throughout May, and we all spent June praying that the farmers would get the hay crop safely indoors. If it rains, and the hay is ruined, the price of the hay automatically begins to climb, and we can all live without that sort of extra expense! Mr. B. sneaked out between showers and bit by bit, as we sighed with relief, the big hay barn began to fill and our next winter's feed supply was safe. Mr. B. grows *beautiful* hay. It is a nice firm hay, not the soft meadowy stuff that horses chomp through in five minutes. It gives them something to chew on, which is important for both their digestion and for their teeth — but

Nanette was getting enormous

of course we would not be feeding the new hay until well into winter, because hay should never be fed to horses "new". It gives them a frightful stomach-ache, or colic, and only the very ignorant do not know the end result of a serious bout of colic — the horse, unable to "belch" or be sick, because his digestive system only permits his food to go one way, rolls about in agony to try to relieve his pain. If he twists a gut, rolling about thus, he can die.

But putting such horrid thoughts aside, because this book is very much about a living mare and foal, we had to keep Rusty and Nanette stabled at night until the end of June. You simply cannot leave a foal out of doors on a dark cold wet night, even though it is June 21, and supposed to be the longest day of the year! Mid-summer came and went without doing much for the reputation of the English weather, but a week later there was a sign of repentence from above, and on June 26 I firmly decided that the foal would have to harden off and live out. I was getting very fed-up with mucking out and, whilst during her early months, Nan had made little difference to the amount of work involved, now that she was getting bigger I was beginning to feel a familiar sensation of backache . . . That Is It, I told Nan, mentally, You Are Now Living Out!

The first time, on the very first evening of this tremendous decision, it was quite dry and pleasant when I put them into the field at 5 p.m. But by 6 p.m. it had clouded over, and was beginning to drizzle slightly. By 10 p.m. it was still drizzling and I felt dreadfully guilty about Nanette in the rain. I telephoned my vet, Sue, who said "don't be silly, it's only summer rain!" OK, that calmed me down; but I could hardly get down to the farm quickly enough in the morning — silly, because mother and daughter were grazing, quite unconcerned by the rain, and I brought them indoors for a feed and to dry off, whereupon the sun promptly came back out again. I couldn't win.

Nan was, all the while, getting enormous. We tried to teach her as much as we could from an early age, and this now included coming out for rides round the farm with Mum.

We hacked Rusty quietly down the lane, round the paddock, popping her over little jumps and wandered down to the stream to splash about in the water with the dogs. Nanette thought this was tremendous fun! She pawed at the water, anxious to see what made the ripples move, and was puzzled. She investigated the banks thoroughly, peering with amazement through some bushes at the nearby cattle. When one of them moved suddenly, she almost went into orbit with shock!

The exercise helped Rusty slowly to put back some muscle, and helped the foal, too. She was sometimes led, we sometimes allowed her to run free alongsides, but always made sure that going out for a hack was *fun*. We hoped she would remember it all, some day in her future, and associate people with *fun* — within reason, of course, because there was a certain amount of discipline involved when we led her, and we hoped that sank in, too.

Included coming for rides

By the time she reached three months, Nanette was 12 hands and 2 inches at the wither, 13 hands at the rump, and 8 hands from the ground to the elbow. I had read somewhere that, if you measure the height of the foal from ground to elbow at three months, and double it, you have its height at maturity. This meant, inexplicably, that Rusty, a 14.2 hands Welsh Cob, had produced a foal to make at least 16 hands — there must be a giant somewhere in her pedigree, we decided. Music Major does, however, tend to throw a nice big foal, and a lot of his offspring were very big.

Nanette was, at the same time, very strong and developing a mind of her own. I was thankful that I had taught her to be tied up, groomed, have her feet picked up and cleaned out, in the first few days of her life. Goodness knows how I would have coped otherwise because, quite suddenly one awful morning, at home, as I leaned over to pick up the Hoover (instead of bending at the knees to lift it), there was a dreadful ping and a stab of pain in my back and I became an Instant Ninety Year Old Lady. It's horrid being 90, I can assure you.

It meant that Nanette's quite natural foal prancing ceased to be a source of

popping Rusty over little jumps

delight. It just tore at my aching spine and nearly sent me spinning round the bend with pain. Rosanna came up with the temporary answer: tie her leadrope loosely to her mother's, so that when she jerks about, or runs forwards at Something Lurking In The Bushes, the tug is taken up by Rusty's leadrope and by poor old Rusty herself — as if she had not already had enough to endure from her naughty child! But it helped, and solved things for the moment.

The mare and foal were still in a field by themselves, so that I could feed them out of doors, and it wasn't necessary to get them in every day. But I was worried. I knew the situation could not last for ever.

It curtailed our rides out completely for the time being. I spent a couple of very miserable weeks, mostly lying in bed, and visiting a physiotherapist who took one look and said "Horses, is it?" when I arrived. His treatment helped, but I do recall lying on my tummy in bed on the day before the Royal Wedding wondering how on earth I was going to be able to watch the nuptials on television from such an indelicate position! Luckily enough, next morning, the inflammation in the spine had subsided enough for me to lie on my back, and I didn't

her feet needed their first trim-up in early July

miss a moment of the coverage! There was something deliciously decadent about watching Royal Weddings on television in bed, sipping champagne and orange juice at the same time!

But the problem of Nanette was not going to go away just because the Prince of Wales had got married, and one of the things I had to decide was, I *must* find a good home for her. It had to be a knowledgeable home, too, and luckily, through my various activities for PONY magazine and HORSE AND RIDER, I had met some extremely nice people in the equestrian world. Through talking to them, and listening to them, I had learned a lot about their methods, and their way of treating horses, and I thought I knew the person I would most like my foal to go to.

There were three people, in fact, but one of them would never consider buying the female of the equine species, another of them would never consider buying foals, and the third person, whilst appearing to most of the world as an eminent lady dressage rider, also ran a pretty successful stud down in the New Forest. I wrote to Mrs. Jennie Loriston-Clarke, about Nanette, and left it for a week for her to consider. To cut a long story to its barest bones, Jennie said "yes", and suffice it to say I was the happiest girl on earth on the morning that she telephoned her agreement through from her hotel at Wembley, where she was competing and showing at the Royal International Horse Show. I felt a deep sense of relief that Nanette was falling into the best, most loving and most capable hands that I could have hoped for — it was the answer to a dream and a prayer!

Nanette with Olaf

Meanwhile, Nanette's education continued, and her feet needed their first trim-up in early July. The "foal toe" and the hoof were getting very long — the foal toe is the name given by some to the amount of hoof a foal has at birth. As the foal starts to feed, and walk about, new hoof growth appears, and as the foal gets more upright on its fetlocks, so the foal toe appears to splay outwards from the new growth, and it should be cut away to allow the feet to grow correctly, and hence the legs to grow correctly.

Derek was naturally pleased to find Nanette quite unconcerned about having her feet lifted in the air, although the cutting sensation made her fidget momentarily, as did the rasping — she stood tied up, as good as gold, and I was so *proud* of her. Derek gave her a playful smack on the bottom, which made me thankful that she was quite used to people giving her playful smacks on the bottom! We did it quite often.

Nanette, Rusty and Olaf

A week later the vet came to give Nan her first anti-tetanus injection. Nanette had been afforded protection against the dreaded tetanus disease (a killer) by the milk of her mother; Rusty is regularly given an anti-tetanus booster injection every September, and this, for the first few weeks, protected Nanette, too. Some people maintain that the practice of giving regular anti-tetanus injections to horses is not necessary, using the argument that you should only inject them when they actually injure themselves. This does not, of course, make allowance for tiny cuts and hidden grazes, because a mere pinprick on barbed wire, or a tread on a sharp 'stone, can let infection into the bloodstream, which may not be noticed until it is too late. I have never thought it worth taking such a chance.

Also, we had now decided, Mr. B. in particular, that the horses should all go into one field. If one of the bigger horses was to kick Nan, or bite her, she needed her anti-tetanus injection for protection. Not that I visualised Rusty letting the bigger horses near her foal, to begin with, at least: she was a natural mother, and would guard her foal against the bigger animals' curious investigations. We also chose this moment to give Nan her first wormer — all horses should be wormed *regularly*, and foals especially.

There was a herd of six horses and ponies in the big field and our plan of campaign was: that Rusty and Nanette should be turned out into the big field first with Olaf, the dun gelding that they lived next door to in the stable block. Then we would turn out the others, Taffy, Shandy, Tango and Lady, leaving the other youngster, Sunny, until last, for them all to become acquainted one by one.

Nanette in the stable yard

. . . and at grass

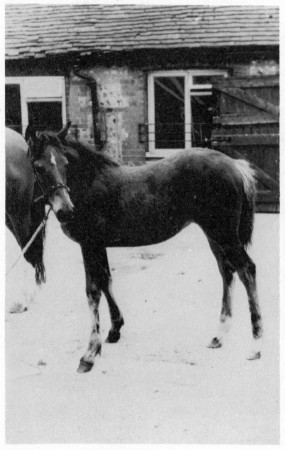

It worked out perfectly, to the letter, and Olaf, as expected, decided that he was the ideal stepfather for Nanette and a substitute husband for Rusty. When the other three geldings went out to join them, he told them very firmly that this was *his* wife and daughter, thank you very much, and would they please make themselves scarce. Rusty underlined his message, approaching them with her fangs bared (I never thought I would see Rusty showing her fangs!); they didn't wait around to see if she meant business.

Gradually, as time went on, the herd became sort of aunts and uncles for Nanette. She grew quite fond of Lady, a big nearly-Thoroughbred mare. I often saw her following Lady round the field on walk-abouts, Rusty grazing unconcernedly, although I expect that beneath all that mane she was keeping a weather eye. She grew less and less bothered with Nanette as time went on, because they were often seen to be grazing a long way apart. But if Nanette lay down to sleep, Rusty, and sometimes Olaf, too, would stand over her, on guard.

Nanette

But during the first few days, Rusty kept herself carefully between her foal and the herd, and if the little band of horses looked like running into a corner, she was clever enough to head the foal safely away from the hedges and back into the open field — it was a vast field, chosen for that very reason. A small paddock, with less area for the horses to run, would have been quite dangerous.

All the while, I continued putting Nanette away on her own sometimes and, prior to the back problems, I even hacked Rusty out away from the farm for an hour. Nanette only called out for as long as she could hear her mother's hoofbeats, and as soon as all was quiet, she quietened down, too. The minute her mother returned, she would give a pretty high-pitched whinney and kick the sides of the stable, as if to say "Get Back In Here and Feed Me!" But I felt it would all help the mare and foal through the painful business of weaning, if they learned to be apart sometimes now.

7

End of a Summer

I could not have got through the summer without the girls at the farm, Lisa and Julia, who gave me so much *physical* assistance. They were a constant source of amusement to me anyway, talking endlessly about their beloved ponies, going off to shows, practising for shows, and when my back became so bad that I could not, quite literally, even lie down on it, they stepped cheerily into the breech. Luckily the summer holidays had begun and Lisa was free to become Keeper of the Mare And Foal until the weaning took place in October.

It *is* necessary in hot weather to bring horses in each day: although they need a certain amount of sun on their backs, they also need shelter from intense heat and the constant buzzing flies which crawl round their eyes and make their eyes swollen, sore and weepy. A field shelter will rarely be used by horses in winter, as they prefer to back up to a hedge or a tree to keep the weather out; but in summer they will make use of a shelter for relief from the heat, and unless they have companions to stand nose-to-tail with, so that they can keep swishing the flies out of each other's eyes, they can be as miserable out in a field in August, if not so hungry, as in January.

Lisa brought the mare and foal in from the field for me each morning; she fed them; gave them hay; filled their water buckets; and each evening, when the flies became less of a nuisance, turned them back out into the field and mucked out the stable. Later, as the backache began to decrease — due in no small way to Lisa's help — I was able to drive down to the farm late on summer evenings to walk the dogs. I would find the stable spotless, the bed laid for the following day, feed already measured into buckets, the water freshly topped up, and clean hay in the corner. I could not have managed without Lisa and, in her absence at Pony Club camp, Julia — they were super.

August turned slowly into September; some long hot days, and cool ones: some thunder storms, and Nanette's rapid growth had slowed down slightly. She was perfectly mannered, Lisa assured me; she was bigger than Lisa, and could have dragged her all over the place, but Rusty had taught her daughter well. You Always Walk Quietly and Obediently, she must have said to Nanette. You Must Not Pull Humans About Or They May Smack You!

So Nan did not pull Lisa about, and I congratulated Rusty on her daughter's upbringing. Foals learn *so* much from their mothers, just by watching them, and copying their behaviour. Nanette had been looking to Rusty for guidance, from the moment she was born. She had watched her mother eat hay, and had copied her and eaten hay for herself. She had learned from her mother that buckets

For Lisa a kiss from Nanette of goodbye and thank you

Lisa with Rusty and Nanette

contain goodies; that grass is there to be eaten; that straw bedding is laid down for you to sleep on; that the water bucket is there to drink from; and goodness knows how many other silent mystical messages had transmitted from Rusty to her foal during the weeks they were together. Precious weeks, moments to be treasured — if only they realised. They were both blissfully unaware that, as August turned into September, both their lives would change, for ever. It was unlikely that they would ever meet again, and if they did, less likely still that they would remember

The author and Nanette

each other.

This precious mother–daughter relationship ended, as all mother–daughter relationships are destined to end in the horse world, when on an October day, Nanette was weaned, finally, from Rustina, and loaded into a horsebox and driven off to what I knew and believed to be the best home I could possibly have found for Rusty's foal. Of my feelings at that time, I cannot speak yet. One day, some day, soon, I shall be able to tell you.

Brian and Nanette

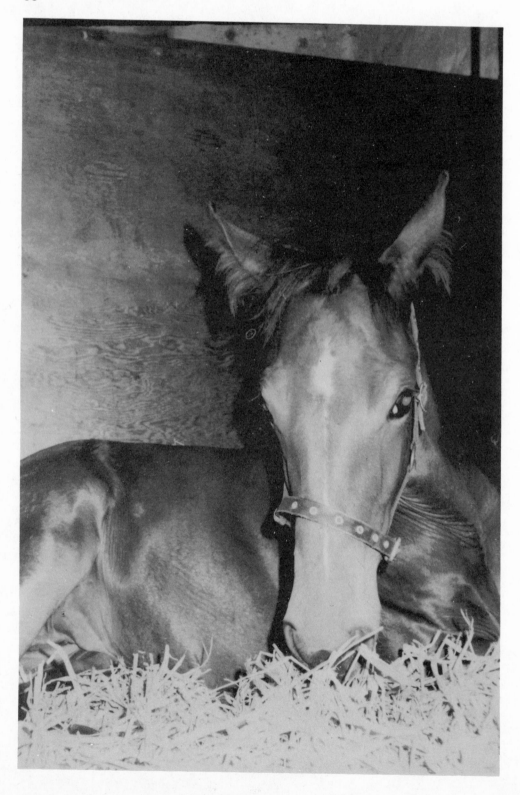

Epilogue

By the time this book is published, Rusty's Foal, Hurst Grange Nanette, will, I devoutly hope, be safely installed in her new home with Jennie Loriston-Clarke, MBE, FBHS, at the Catherston Stud in the beautiful New Forest. This, I hope, is where Rusty's foal will grow up, where she will be eventually broken in, ridden and, possibly even one day, have a foal of her own. She is now living in a Stud run by one of the best riders in the world, and her husband, Anthony, with their two daughters Anne and Lizzie, who are tremendously interested both in the activities of the Stud, and the riding of the horses.

Although I bred Rusty's foal, our beloved Nanette, to keep for myself and ride one day, this was not to be, and it would have been morally wrong of me to try and keep a horse that I was not physically fit to bring on properly, handle properly, and ride properly. Her mother, the placid cob to end all placid cobs —

we always say God threw the mould away after he had built Rusty — Mrs. Tiggy-winkle, the Original Family Pony, or What Have You Got There, is all the horse I shall ever need. When Rusty goes, I shall just have to drive off down to Wales and try my best to find another one like her. The dream of riding and owning her foal was simply not to be.

But Jennie has granted me "visiting rights" to see Nanette, and I shall be popping down to the New Forest three times a year to take photographs, and write up progress reports for PONY magazine . . . and maybe, in time, another book!

What I secretly hope, and she won't know it until she gets time to read this book, is that one day, in the not too far distant future, Jennie will allow me one, small, short ride — on Nanette. Rusty's Foal.

Reference
Encyclopaedia of the Horse
(Edited by E. Hartley Edwards, published 1977, Octopus Books Limited, London)

NANETTE'S Diary   **The First Six Months**

Born:	approx. 5 a.m., April 21, 1981
First Groomed:	April 21, 1981
First Steps:	April 23, 1981
First Time Feet Done:	April 25, 1981
First Walk Out:	April 29, 1981
First In Field:	May 5, 1981
First Show:	Hickstead, May 29, 1981 — Best Foal Rosette, Mountain and Moorland
First Tetanus:	June 25, 1981
First Wormer:	June 25, 1981 (Strongid-P)
Second Wormer:	July 29, 1981 (1 sachet Panacur)
Second Tetanus:	End August 1981 (booster)
Turned Out with Other Horses:	End July 1981
Third Wormer:	September 8, 1981
Weaned:	October 1981

Nanette